By Tara Rachel Jones

IT'S TIME FOR YOGA

Illustrated by Aaron Livingston Jones

A LITTLE BOUNDER BOOKS BOOK

DEDICATION

I dedicate this book to my grandfather, Peter G. Scotese whose life
is my living definition of integrity and whose faith in me goes beyond
measure. For my husband Aaron, who lovingly labored to illustrate the grace
of the practice through the playful interaction between human and nature
in his unique and original artistry, and to my sweet daughter, Jade Rose.

I offer this book to the children with whom I have watched grow over
the past 15 years through our practice of yoga together and whose
imagination and play have inspired the poetry and creative expression
in this book.

Published in 2011 by Little Bounder Books
PO Box 122
Lincoln, MA 01773
www.littlebounderbooks.com

Graphic Design: Alexa Castle
www.alexacastle.com

ISBN 978-0-615-45151-0

The publisher and the author disclaim
any liability associated with the use
of the information in this book. Always
consult a physician before starting
a new exercise program.

TABLE OF CONTENTS

ABOUT THE AUTHOR & THE ILLUSTRATOR

Tara Rachel Jones, M.Ed. has developed her own approach to children's yoga which is simply yet uniquely: a synthesis of education, developmental movement, and yogic teachings. Trained and experienced in the teaching of Public, Private, Montessori and Waldorf education, she has been a pioneer of children's yoga in the Boston area. Her training and inspiration to bring yoga to children came from Sarabess Forster, her beloved yoga teacher. She started teaching yoga to children in her Montessori classroom in 1993 and has been teaching yoga to young people from nursery school through high school ever since.

For more about Tara Rachel's classes see www.floweryoga.com and for more information about her courses for children, youth, teens and aspiring children's yoga teachers see www.thewisdomgarden.com.

Aaron Livingston Jones is a visual artist and long time teacher of yoga. He resides in the Boston area with his wife Tara Rachel and their daughter, Jade Rose. He dedicates the art in this book to the loving memory of Bryan C. McNamire.

For more information about Aaron's art see www.aaronlivingstonjones.com.

ACKNOWLEDGMENTS

I give gratitude to my masterful teachers of yoga: Sarabess Forster whom
showed me the art of combining education and yogic teachings; The
International Sivananda Yoga Vedanta Centers whom have given me a home
for my own yoga education and teachings for teens and families for the past
15 years; Fundacion' Indra Devi in Buenos Aires Argentina for my studies
of organic gardening and teaching children; Baron Baptiste for the experience
of inspiring yoga to become a mainstream initiative; Barbara Benagh for
giving me roots and wings as a teacher and practitioner; Arthur Kilmurray
for guiding me to explore the mysteries of human development; Tias Little
for his precision and reverence; Zoe Stewart for her devotion and to my
anatomy teachers Bonnie Bainbridge Cohen for her presence and experiential
approach to developmental movement; Yaron Gal Carmel for his insatiable
curiosity about structural anatomy and boundless sense of wonder;
and to all nursery, grammar and high schools, yoga studios and families
in the Boston area that have invited me to bring this practice to children,
youth, teens and adults.

I wish to honor the many paths of learning that reflect my training
and experience in the field of education: Public Education, Montessori
Education and Waldorf Education. I have been blessed with a unique
journey that included the study, certification and experience teaching
in these environments. I am also grateful to Jason Gordon and the
Alchemical Courtyard for the experience of writing and designing
an educational outline and vision for a holistic school for grades N-8.

Thanks to Stona Fitch of The Concord Free Press for supporting
the publication of this book.

Thank you to Alexa Castle for her enthusiasm and wholehearted interest
in this project. Her graphic design expertise and creative ingenuity have
enhanced the beauty of the artwork presented in this book!

A very special thank you to Chip Hartranft of The Arlington Center
for his support housing my classes at The Arlington Center and for referring
me as a children's yoga teacher to the surrounding schools and organizations
in the Boston area!

A NOTE FOR PARENTS & TEACHERS

It's Time for Yoga is a unique yoga book made especially for children! The sequencing of the illustrated yoga postures in this book strongly resemble that of Sivananda Yoga and the developmental movement patterns of the human body in the first year of life - from the ground to standing.

Encourage children to examine the illustrations in this picture book. Follow their natural inclination to imitate and say "I can do it". Invite them to tell their own stories about the animals and habitats illustrated on each page.

Songs and rhythmical verses may be memorized. The verses with each posture are written to include the "spirit medicine" of the natural environments depicted. The verses can be taught line by line in a call and response mode.

Play a memory game. As children get to know the verses, you read the verse and they silently make the postures.

Dance to the Sun. Have fun making the animal sounds that go with each pose in this sequence (see page 10). A developmental approach to the classical Sun Salutations, this dance has evolved over 15 years of practice with young children. The sequence is doable and kind to the adult body as well.

Use the Little Glossary and Appendices for deeper understanding. See Little Appendix C for detailed instructions for the Dance to the Sun and all of the illustrated postures.

When playing with the book, be sure to follow these guidelines:

a. Practice on yoga mats or a carpeted area without shoes and socks.
b. If you or the children seem unsure about how to get into or out of a posture, read the instructions for the postures in the back of the book.
c. Follow the instructions carefully, when needed and ALWAYS move slowly.
d. Turn off any music/television before you play. Allow the silence to create the space for imagination to soar!
e. Before attempting this or any form of exercise, always consult a physician/and or your child's pediatrician or specialist.
f. Always take into consideration the ages and individual needs of the children when using this book.
g. Do not use this book as a form of physical therapy.

Now… IT'S TIME FOR YOGA!

IT'S TIME FOR YOGA

- sung to the tune of Frere Jacques

It's time for yoga.

It's time for yoga.

We are one.

We are one.

Loving all the animals.

Loving all
the plants.

And all our friends.

Namasté.

8

Namasté. Namasté.

I am light.

You are light.

I shine my light
to you.

You shine your
light to me.

Namasté. Namasté.

Let us make a dance for the sun, inviting all the animals to join in our fun!

DANCE TO THE SUN

We grow the corn up to the sun

and plow when the harvest is done.

12

I open my gills wide and free,

and flow from the river to the sea.

I pull you and you pull me.

I give, you give.

We are friends, you see.

17

I spread my wings with wonder and delight,

your color and beauty make our world so bright.

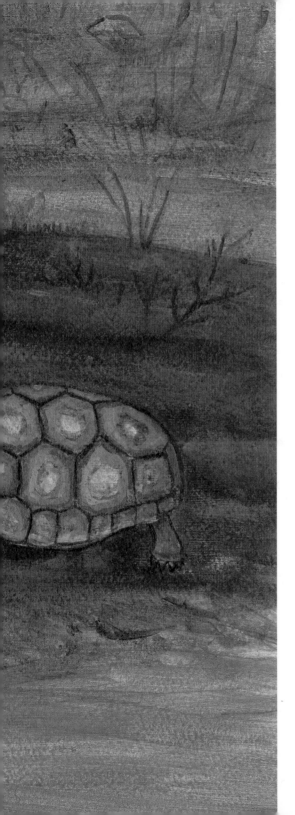

I hover down and make my shell,

to meet the turtle who has wisdom to tell.

Upon the sand you glide,

protector of the sea.

I lift up high and make my shell.

From side to side I go as well.

Sacred mother of the earth,

we stand strong on the grass.

In peace we allow life to pass.

Sojourner in the hot desert sand,

I meet you with my hump so grand.

I stretch my tongue and roar with might.

Strong and daring, quite a sight!

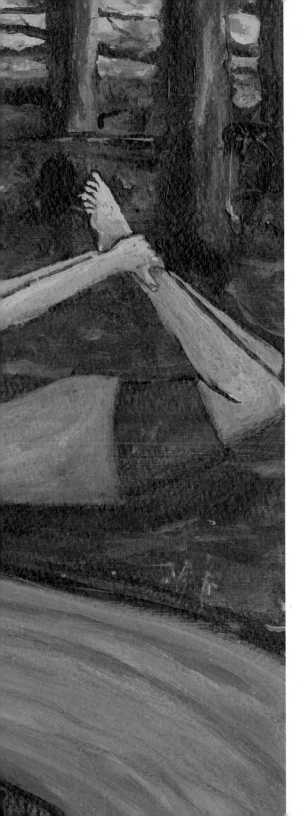

Row, row, row, my bow,

journey down the stream,

follow life's ceaseless flow,

and realize every dream.

Divine flower,

your path is one truth to be told.

Your shoot reaches to the sun.

My petals and yours are one.

Healer and guardian, I hear your caw

and lift myself up before you with awe.

You are soft and supple inside

with a swirled hard house

upon your back.

Silent friend, I twist my spine,

in honor of thine.

Firmly you grasp the ground,

yet your boughs sway so high.

You bear fruit, seed, and flower.

You offer so much to bird, squirrel, and me.

I balance in the likeness of your power.

Soaring high - so much to see,

oh messenger who rides the wind.

I spread my wings and fly with thee.

Gentle and kind, a symbol of love,

I stand in stillness, with heart open,

while my arms rise with grace above.

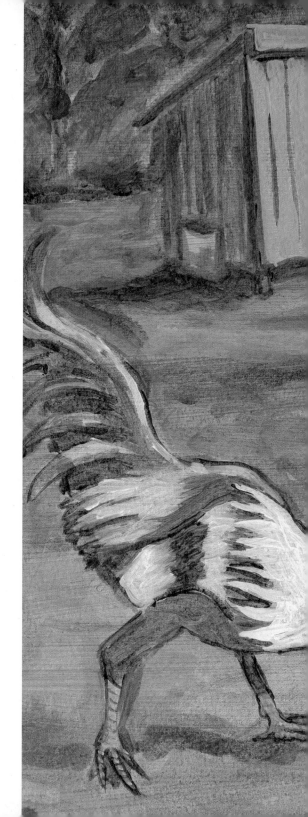

You offer an egg,

a symbol of life I know well.

I bow to you and the golden light

within each shell.

We stand firm with arms and legs long.

Tilting ourselves majestic and strong.

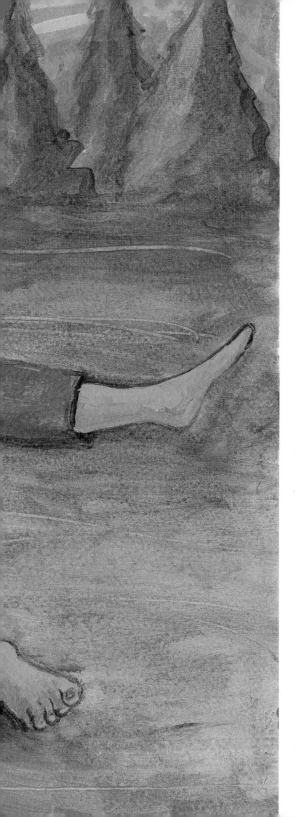

This is the way you belly breathe.

This is the way you belly breathe.

This is the way you belly breathe,

in and out of your nose.

Feel your belly move up and down.

Feel your belly move up and down.

Feel your belly move up and down,

when you belly breathe.

- to the tune of *Here We Go Round the Mulberry Bush*.

49

Still, silent, and serene.

My mind like the river flows in peace,

to follow my heart.

LITTLE GLOSSARY

DEFINITIONS

OM The sound "aum" symbolizes the harmony of all creation. It is known as a Bija (seed) Mantra (energy encased in sound).

NAMASTÉ *I Shine my Light* is a song by Tara R. Jones that shares the meaning of Namasté (page 9).

SANSKRIT Sanskrit is the language of yoga. It is an ancient scriptural language that is most commonly chanted or sung.

SAVASANA Relaxed, deep breathing and rest; *This is the Way We Belly Breath* is a song by Tara R. Jones to promote relaxation (page 48).

YOGA Yoga literally means "to yoke" or to bring balance in all aspects of life relating to the body, mind and spirit. For children, a yoga practice offers tools for attentiveness, self-regulation and connection to themselves, community and the natural world. *It's Time for Yoga* is a song by Tara R. Jones that shares the meaning of yoga (page 8).

ENGLISH NAMES TO SANSKRIIT

DANCE TO THE SUN (page10)............ Variations of Surya Namaskara

1. Give Thanks .... Namaskara
2. Reach for the Sky .... Urdhva Hasta Tadasana
3. Touch the Earth .... Uttanasana
4. Baby Cow .... Gavasana
5. Cobra .... Bhujangasana
6. Swan .... Raja Bhujangasana
7. Silent Fox .... Puccha (tail)
8. Cat .... Marjariasana
9. Dog .... Adho Mukha Svanasana
10. Frog .... variation of Malasana
11. Bird .... variation of Dekasana
12. Mountain .... Tadasana

Bow Boats	Dhanurasana
Butterfly	Baddha Konasana
Camel	Ustrasana
Chicken	variation of Parsvottanasana
Cornstalk	Salamba Sarvangasana
Cow	Gavasana
Crab	variation of Purvottanasana
Crow	Bakasana/Kakasana
Deer	variation of Virabhadrasana I
Fish	Matsyendrasana
Flower	variation of Dwi Hasta Bujasana
Hawk	Dekasana
Lion	Simhasana
Meditation	Padmasana
Plow	Halasana
Pyramid	Trikonasana
Relaxation	Savasana
Seesaw	variation of Upavistha Konasana
Snail Shell	variation of Marichyasana I & III
Tortoise	Kurmasana
Tree	Vriksasana

PEACEFUL PLACE
Savasana

Lay down on your back. Start to belly breath. Imagine now that your breath is the wind and you are resting on a puffy soft cloud - cozy. Off you go high into the sky, sailing away through the air. No worries need to follow you. Drop them down into the worry river below. There you go, floating across the blue sky. As you pass a tall mountain you can see an eagle in its nest. There is a hawk, soaring in the wind! The geese are flying by and you see the smaller birds hopping in the trees below. There is a beautiful waterfall by the trees. Your cloud is landing there. Amidst the soft moss, you rest. The sunlight shimmers on the mist from the waterfall and makes a rainbow!

Imagine now a soft rainbow blanket covering you. Feel the color red rolling over your toes, feet, legs and hands - relaxing your toes, feet, legs and hands. Feel the color orange rolling over your hips, your lower belly and your forearms - relaxing your hips, your lower belly and your forearms. Feel the color yellow rolling over your belly and your upper arms - relaxing your belly and your upper arms. Feel the color green rolling over your heart, your chest and your shoulders - relaxing you heart, your chest and your shoulders. Feel the color light blue rolling over your neck and your chin - relaxing your neck and your chin. Feel the color indigo (dark blue) rolling over your face and forehead - relaxing your face and your forehead. Feel the color violet rolling over the top of your head and your hair - relaxing the top of your head and your hair. Feel your belly move up and down as you breathe. Feel the rainbow dance and swirl in you. Your puffy cloud is lifting you back up into the sky and sailing you back to where you came from. After 12 more breaths, you will be home. Wiggle your fingers and toes. Give yourself a little hug. Pull your knees in close to your heart and wrap your arms around your legs. Roll over to the right side. Sit up. Now you have arrived right at home inside yourself!   Sing: Om Shanti, Shanti Shanti - peace-peace-peace.

A PROMISE TO THE EARTH
Special Affirmation for Meditation

I promise to the earth
    to cherish every living thing,
        to care for earth and sea and air,
            with peace and freedom everywhere.

Adapted from a Peace poem- NMI-1997

SILENT PLACE
Dhyana

Sit on a cushion in an easy chair pose (Sukasana), Half lotus (Ardha Padmasana) or full Lotus (Padmasana). Place your hands on the roots of your body tree (hips) - fingers in the front and thumbs in the back. Use your thumbs to gently press the back of you body tree roots forward until you feel your body tree trunk (back bones) get long and tall and your branches (ribs and shoulders) feel full and wide. Then relax your hands on your knees with palms up and your index fingers and thumbs touching (Jnana Mudra).

Now sit still - not stiff - and let the wind blow through your branches. Start to breath slowly in and out, in and out, in and out. Keep letting the wind expand your branches - growing taller with each breath in and each breath out.

You are sitting in the grass near a river. It is not too cold, not too hot. It feels just right. The grass is soft and comfortable. You sit here listening to the flowing water of the river and the songs of the birds. The sun is shining. It is just rising and you sit still as it wakes up the world. Just in front of you there are some flowers. Their petals still closed from the night. As the first rays of light fall upon the flowers, the petals begin to open. The more brightly the sun shines, the more the petals open and bloom. Here come the bees

58

and the butterflies, sipping nectar from the flowers. Because you are still, you can see the bees land and drink from each flower. You can see the splendor of colors on the butterflys' wings. The birds' songs grow more delightful as you sit and breathe with the sound of the flowing river.

The day has gone by, the sun is now setting. You watch the flowers close their petals to go to sleep. The water rushing seems to be singing a song - a song of harmony. Listen and sing along:

Om, Om, Om, shanti shanti, shanti, peace, peace, peace.

Open your eyes at home where you began. Bring peace and harmony wherever you go.

THE 5 POINTS OF YOGA
Yoga Philosophy for Daily Living

By Swami Vishnu Devananda - Founder of the Sivananda Yoga Vedanta Centers and Ashrams Worldwide

1. Proper Exercise - Hatha Yoga: Asanas (postures).

2. Proper Relaxation -Yoga Nidra: Savasana (yoga sleep-conscious guided relaxation).

3. Proper Breathing - Pranayama: Guided breathing practices breath control.

4. Proper Diet: Local, organic whole foods diet based strongly in vegetables, nuts, legumes, whole grains, and whole or raw dairy.

5. Positive Thinking - Kirtan and Dhyana: Singing (Kirtan) uplifting songs or chants in English or Sanskrit, repetition of mantras or affirmations, and meditation (Dhyana - silence, stillness, peace flowing down the river of the mind).

THE 4 PATHS TO YOGA
Basic Yoga Philosophy

Karma Yoga: The path of dedication to all work for a higher purpose rather than personal gain. The practice of selfless service. This could be doing chores, helping those in need, or supporting family members.

Bhakti Yoga: The path of transforming emotion towards the truth through ritual and humility. The experience of love and devotion through artistic activities like song (chanting), dance, media arts, listening to stories, drama and prayer.

Raja Yoga: A systematic approach to settling the fluctuations and distractions of the mind towards higher states of consciousness. The practice of cultivating a sturdy body and mind so as to merge one's awareness with the wonder of life. Children can learn these accessible tools for self-motivation and confidence in all life pursuits.

Jnana Yoga: The path of intellectual development and spiritual evolution; the pursuit of knowledge through study, inquiry, analysis, experimentation and experience. It is the most difficult and direct path of practice that involves right inquiry (Vichara) and constant self-analysis (Viveka - discrimination). This path is sharpened by the refinement of practice of the first three paths. The child attends some aspect of a directed quest towards learning at home and school.

RAJA YOGA
The Eight Limbed Path

Raja Yoga is also named the eight (Asthanga) limbed path. While yoga is all-inclusive of multicultural and universal beliefs, the first two limbs of the practice of Raja Yoga outline some basic character building principles that offer a positive intention, attitude and foundation for the other limbs. These principles offer a container by which children can learn and experience - through practice - the benefits of a healthy yoga practice. The eight-limbed path is as follows:

1. Yama: Modifications of attitude and behavior to support universal needs for safety - mentally, emotionally, and spiritually.

Ahimsa: Non-injury by random acts of kindness, sharing, forgiveness, compassion, caring for the environment and all living beings and offering love and friendship to those in need, family and friends. Learning - through modeling and practice - how to communicate feelings, needs and requests with awareness and caring language.

Satya: Truthfulness in all aspects of life and having the courage to be truthful about one's feelings and needs and the feelings and needs of others.

Asteya: Non-stealing by showing gratitude, asking permission, having a willingness to support the success of others, big heartedness and charity.

Brahmacharya: Temperance and moderation in life's explorations, particularly with polarities. Discovering when enough is enough through trial, error and life experience.

Aparigraha: Non-clinging to more than one's needs. Developing discernment about what one's needs really are. Becoming conscious about ways to take care of what one has. The willingness to acknowledge appreciation and give selflessly to others.

2. Nyamas: Rhythms, rituals and practices for deepening self-development.

Saucha: Purity and cleanliness practiced as part of the daily routine of life; bathing, brushing teeth, wearing clean clothing, combing one's hair, cleaning one's room, resting well, eating well, exercising, spending time out in nature.

Santosha: Experiencing contentment with one's self by honoring one's own boundaries and the boundaries of others; finding the inner strength to find confidence and ease in times of adversity as well as serenity.

Tapas: Cultivating self-discipline by learning in a developmentally prepared environment with dignified role models who inspire innate curiosity and motivation to emerge through interactive study.

Svadyaya: Deepening a knowing of one's self through art, journaling, communicating with trusted mentors about one's struggles and triumphs, and reading about people whose actions have brought about change.

Ishvara-Pradnidhana: Cultivating faith in one's sense of spirit and honoring the same sense of spirit in others and a willingness to bring the best of yourself to each new situation and trust in the unknown.

3. Asana: (Hatha Yoga) Practicing postures that nourish the proper function of the physical body, balance emotions and awaken the spirit.

4. Pranayama: Exploring various breathing techniques that balance the nervous system and bring equanimity and higher awareness to the mind.

5. Pratyahara: Lowering the external stimulus in one's environment and cultivating discernment and rhythms around cycles of action and rest - stimulus and quiet.

6. Dharana: Developing concentration by doing just one activity at a time and eliminating the habit of multitasking. Exploring practices where one focuses on an affirmation, the word peace, the mantra OM (AUM) and repeating it over and over for a period of time.

7. Dhyana: Meditation and developing an awareness and understanding of the intuition. This can be enhanced by spending time in nature everyday.

8. Samadhi: Contemplation and the acute sense of one's connection to all living beings through selfless service, extended time in nature, deep meditation and fulfillment through the flow of LOVE.

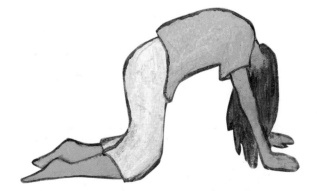

THE SUN DANCE 10
Surya Namaskara

Let us do a dance in honor of the sun.
inviting the animals to join in our fun!

1. Gather some sunshine into your heart and say: Namaste'. Bring palms together at the heart.

2. Reach up to the sky.

3. And touch the earth (fold forward).

4. Be the cow: Step one foot back and the other foot back, put your knees down, and be on all fours.

5. The silent fox: Lift one arm extended out and your opposite leg to make the tail. Repeat with your other arm and your other leg (contra-lateral limb-raising).

6. The cobra: Bring hips forward, bend arms and let belly touch the floor. Press your palms down and lift your head and chest, keep your elbows bent and close to your sides.

7. The swan: Bend your knees and lift your head to look up and make a long swan neck.

8. The cat: Push down with your hands and lift your hips back onto all fours, then round your back, and drop your head and your tail.

9. The dog: Push down with your hands and lift your knees and hips up high.

10. The frog: Jump your feet to your hands.

11. The bird: Stay in a squat, bring your knees together, come on to your tip toes, bring your arms back at your sides like wings, slowly rise up to standing, balancing on your tippy toes, with your arms out to the sides like wings.

12. The mountain: Stand up tall with your feet together and your arms at your sides.

Benefits: Increases heart rate and the circulation of fresh oxygenated blood through the body. Aides in warming the muscles and joints to increase flexibility and range of motion for the asana practice. Steadies the rhythm of the breath and mental focus.

Notes: Breathe in for poses that lift you up from the earth and breath out for poses that bring you closer to the ground. Do at least three rounds of the sun dance. Gradually work up to 6, 9 and 12 rounds. Great to practice when you wake up in the morning and on those rainy and snowy days that keep you inside.

BOW BOATS
Dhanurasana

Lie down on your belly, bend your knees and take hold of the tops of your feet. Try to keep your knees closer together.

Step 1. Press your feet into your hands and feel you head and shoulders lift up. Keep looking at the ground to open the back of your neck.

Step 2. Gently press your hips down as you continue to push your feet into your hands and lift your toes and knees up.

Step 3. Rock your bow boat. Breath in as you rock back and breathe out as you go foreword. AVOID using your head to make the rocking motion.

Benefits: Tones the entire spine. Opens the chest and the front of the thighs and hips.

Notes: Try to keep your legs and feet parallel. Lift your chest before you lift your head. Avoid pushing your chin forward and keep the back of the neck long.

BUTTERFLY
Baddha Konasana

Sit on your bum with your legs straight. Bend one knee out to the side, then the other. Put your feet together. Extend your arms out to the side at shoulder height and slowly flap your wings for 3-6 breaths.

Benefits: Increases the range of motion and blood circulation in the hips, releases muscles on the inner legs and the lower back.

Notes: Avoid bouncing your knees up and down. Pretend your mouth is like the straw-like tongue of the butterfly. Sip nectar from a flower making the butterfly breath (Sitali).

You can purse your lips like you are sucking from a straw OR Curl your tongue like a straw. Breathe in through your pursed lips or your tongue, close your mouth and breathe out through your nose. Take 3-6 sips. Feel the cooling sensation of butterfly breathing!

CAMEL 26
Ustrasana

Sit with your knees bent on your feet (tops of your feet down). Lift your hips and stand on your knees. Turn your toes down on the ground.

Begin with your chin closer to your chest, hands at your sides. Lift your chest to your chin to open your shoulders and stretch your belly out.

Stay there OR try to reach one hand back at a time to touch your heels. You can keep your chin forward OR Let your forehead face the sky. Take 3-6 breaths.

Benefits: Opens the front of the thighs, brings blood circulation to the entire back and opens up the chest.

Notes: Make sure you lift and open your chest before gently bringing your hips forward. Pushing your hips forward first will not be comfortable. Beginners (and young children ages 2-5): keep your hands on your hips and keep your chin to your chest when you make the pose.

CHICKEN
Variation of Parsvottanasana

Start in mountain pose (Tadasana), then step your feet out 2-3 feet apart. Bring your hands to your sides to make chicken wings. Open your right foot out and turn your hips to the right as you bring your left heel back. Keep your left heel on the ground. Breathe in and open your chicken chest. As you breathe out, move your chest forward to peck for corn. Bring your torso parallel to the ground. Take 3-6 breaths.

Lift your chest upright, turn around the other way and repeat the posture on the left side.

Benefits: Opens the muscles on the back of the legs and the back. Opens the chest and shoulders.

CORNSTALK
Salamba Sarvangasana

Approach 1: Lay down on your back with your arms down by your sides, palms down. Push your arms and palms down and lift your knees to your chest. Push down with your arms and hands as you bring your toes over head and your hips lift. Bend your arms and place your hands fingers facing one another, on your hips. Then lift one leg at a time up. Keep your chin at the center of your chest, look up to your toes or close your eyes and take 3-6 slow breaths.

Approach 2: (For younger children-under 6.) Lay down on your back with your arms down by your sides, palms down. Push down with your arms and slowly swing both legs up, point your toes to the ceiling and roll back down. Repeat this action 3-6. times. Avoid going fast! Keep your chin in the center.

Approach 3: Use a wall. Lay down with your legs up the wall, arms at your sides, and palms up. Keep your chin in the center. Bend your knees and place the soles of the feet on the wall. Push into your arms, hands and feet and slowly breathe in and lift your hips up as high as comfortable. Breathe out and lower your hips down. Repeat this cycle 3-6 times. Light the candle and blow it out!

Benefits: Helps recirculate the blood, massages lungs and heart, relaxes the neck and shoulders, and aides in the proper function of the thyroid, and parathyroid glands in your throat. The glands are the "keys" the regulate the global function of the body.

Notes: Children under the age of 12 (ideally 14-15) should not hold this posture for more than 6 breaths at a time. DO NOT TURN the neck from side to side.

COW 24
Gavasana

Sit with yours knees bent on your feet (tops of the feet down). Bring your hands forward on the ground under your shoulders with fingers spread out wide and knees under your hips. Lift your head and relax your belly down. Take 3-6 Moo Breaths!

Benefits: Relaxes the lower back and belly. Strengthens the arms.

Notes: Avoid dropping the belly to low.

CRAB 22
Variation of Purvottanasana

Sit on your bum with knees bent and your feet on the floor. Place your hands behind you with fingers facing forward (or back). Push down with your hands and feet, then lift your hips

up. Let your forehead face the sky.
Take 3-6 breaths.

Benefits: Increases circulation through
the muscles of the back. Stretches the
muscles in the front of the torso and
upper legs. Strengthens the wrists.

Notes: Lift your chest higher before
your lift your hips. Make a pinching
crab. Lift one leg straight up and move
your toes like the pincers. (Thank you
Lauren Worsch!)

Benefits: Relaxes lower back and belly.
Strengthens the arms.

Notes: Avoid -dropping the belly
to low.

CROW 34
Kakasana: Bakasana

Start in Mountain pose, squat down,
and open your knees. Place your arms

to the inside of your knees. Place your
palms down, shoulder-width distance
apart, on the ground. Open your
fingers. Lift your heels up and slightly
lift your hips. Work to bring your
shins onto the back of your upper
arms. Bring your knees and arms
toward one another as you round your
back, raise your head, look forward
and lift your toes off the ground.
Take 3-5 breaths while you fly!

Benefits: Strengthens arms and
belly organs.

Notes: Try this pose by lifting only
one foot at a time. Keep your head up.

DEER 42
Variation of Virabhadrasana I

Start in mountain pose (Tadasana).
Put your hands on your hips, bend
your right knee as you step your left
leg back. Raise your arms up over your

head and bring your palms together to make deer antlers. Take 3-5 breaths. Bring your hands back on your hips as you step your left leg forward. Repeat the posture on the other side.

Benefits: Opens the chest and helps deep breathing. Strengthens feet and legs.

Notes: Look forward at first and when your balance is strong, try to look up to your hands.

FISH 14
Matsyendrasana

Sit up on your bum with your legs out straight. Place your hands, palms down under your bum. With elbows pointing back, bend your arms and put your elbows and forearms on the floor. Keep your head up and look at your toes as you push up your chest (puff-up your fish gills). Keep your

head up and make a fish face. Older children: put your head back and rest the top of your head on the floor. Take 3-6 slow breaths.

Benefits: This is a counterpose to the shoulderstand and the plow. You are bending your neck in the opposite direction. Increases lung capacity by opening the chest. Opens tight shoulders e.g. from carrying a backpack.

Notes: Be sure to keep your hips down. Lift and open your chest BEFORE you relax your head back. Be sure your hands are under your bottom, with palms down before you start to put your elbows down.

FLOWER 32
Variation of Dwi Hasta Bujasana

Sit on your bum with straight legs, bend your knees and place your hands between your feet. With your knees bent, lift your feet. Swing your arms under your knees and open your hands facing forward. Try to balance with your feet in the air. Smell your flower with 3-6 breaths!

Benefits: Enhances concentration, coordination and balance. Tones the belly muscles.

Notes: Start to learn to balance by making a flower bud. Sit on your bum, lift your feet up and hold them together with your hands as you balance on your bum.

HAWK 40
Dekasana (variation of Virabhadrasana III)

Stand in mountain pose. Keeping your arms at your sides, open your palms to face forward and step the left leg back. Keep your chest open as you lift your leg higher. Always keep your chest a little higher than your back leg as you look forward. Take 3-6 breaths while you soar! Repeat the pose, taking the right leg back.

Benefits: Strengthens feet, legs and belly. Increases self-confidence. Always look in one direction at eye level (Dristhi).

Notes: Avoid locking your knee when you explore your balance on one leg. Spread out your toes.

LION 28
Simhasana

Sit with your knees bent on your feet (tops of your feet down). Bring your hands forward on the ground - your hands under your shoulders with fingers spread out wide and fingers curled down to make lion paws and your knees under your hips. Lift your head, breathe in through your nose, open your mouth, stick out your tongue, open your eyes, look up between the eye brows or look to the tip of the nose (a gazing point is called a Dristhi) and ROAR as you breathe out! Make 3-6 roar breaths.

Benefits: Relieves tension in the chest and face. Good to practice when you need to let out frustration, tension and anxiety.

Notes: The roar is a big HA sound! Like a loud whisper.

MEDITATION 50
Lotus: Padmasana

Start sitting in a simple cross legged posture (easy chair - Sukasana). Pick up your right foot and cradle your right foot into the crease of your left elbow. Hug your right knee with your right arm. Try to clasp your hands together as you rock your baby (leg) in your arms from side to side. Sing *Rock-A-Bye-Baby*, as a classical nursery rhyme or the *Positively Mother Goose* (Diana Loomins) way: "Rock-a-bye baby on the tree top. When the wind blows, the cradle will rock. Birdies and squirrels will be at play and you can watch them all through the day." Now release the clasp of your hands and bring your right arm to the inside your right leg. Clasp your right foot with both of your hands AND... touch your baby toes to your chin, to your nose, to your left ear and to your right ear! Now try to put your baby foot over your right shoulder (try to bring your right leg over your right shoulder) and wave to another baby foot (of your parent or friends). You might like to try to give your baby a hug and try to put your lower leg and foot behind your neck. NOW...Let's put the baby on our lap. With your right knee still bent, take your right foot and place it on your left thigh close to your left hip.

This is Half Lotus (Ardha Padmasana). This might be enough OR you can invite your other baby to sit on your lap too! Lean forward and slowly lift your left foot and lower leg and allow the leg to cross over the right lower leg as you put your left foot near your right hip. Some left foot babies will say "no thank you". NEVER FORCE your second baby to sit in your lap - only if it feels good. Now repeat - starting with the other baby (left leg).

Benefits: The rocking motion helps to increase the range of motion in the hips and stretch the muscles of the outer leg. When the hips are relaxed, the posture can relieve stiffness in the knees and ankles. Increases blood circulation in the hips and the lower back. Brings the mind focus and serenity.

Notes: Pay close attention to the sensations in the knees when trying this posture. When the range of motion in the hips is limited, the knee joint can be compromised in attempting this posture. DO NOT force your body into this pose as injury can occur in the knees. The starting position (Sukasana) for this posture is a fine way to sit. Practice rock the baby posture as one way of increasing the range of motion in the hips. Young children delight in getting into this pose. By age 10-11, some children need more time and reminders to slow down in their attempt to try the Full Lotus.

PLOW 12
Halasana

Lie down on your back with your arms down by your sides, palms down. Push your arms and palms down and lift your knees to your chest. Push down with your arms and hands as you bring your toes, legs, then hips over your head. Let your toes touch the floor behind you. Bend your arms and place your hands with fingers facing one another or facing up on your hips. Lift your hips, bring your elbows closer together and take 3-6 slow breaths.

Benefits: Gives a long stretch to the muscles in your back and the back of your legs. Strengthens your neck and shoulders. All the organs in your belly and chest get a yoga squeeze. A yoga squeeze helps increase blood circulation. The more the blood circulates freely through your body, the more relaxed you will feel. being relaxed is a feeling of calmness. Turning our bodies upside down is a tool for peace of mind.

Notes: You can separate your feet and bend your knees on each side of your ears, making bunny tail (Karna Pidasana). Do not turn the neck from side to side.

PYRAMID
Triangle: Trikonasana

Start in mountain pose (Tadasana), then step your feet out, parallel at 3-3.5 feet apart. Open your right foot out. Breathe in and raise and extend your arms at shoulder height, breathe out and tip your torso over to the right. While keeping your arms extended, touch your right thigh or shin with your right hand - right palm open - and look up to your left thumb. Take 3 breaths and then come up to standing on a breath in. Bring your feet parallel again. Then turn your left foot out and repeat the posture on the left side.

Benefits: Tones the feet and legs. Strengthens belly and chest. Opens the side muscles of the legs and torso. Increases flexibility in the neck.

Notes: When you tip your torso, move from the hips NOT the waist. You may need to bend the front knee just a little to increase the range of motion in your hips. Look down at first to maintain balance or if you have any discomfort in your neck. Look up to challenge your balance and open your chest more.

RELAXATION 48
Savasana

Lie down on your back. Open your palms with the tops of your hands on the floor. Arms extended out like wings at your sides below the heart level. Separate your feet hips-width distance apart.

Benefits: Soothes and clams the nervous system and the mind. Promotes deep breathing and blood circulation throughout the whole body.

Exercise: Let's play SQUEEZE-N-DROP! Squeeze your toes, feet, legs, hips, lift your bum AND DROP!

Squeeze your fingers, arms, shoulders to your ears, lift your chest AND DROP! Squeeze the muscles in your face to your nose (raisin face) and DROP.

NOW ...OPEN AND DROP! Open your toes, stretch your feet and legs. Open your fingers, stretch your hands, arms, shoulders. Open your eyes, open your mouth wide, and stick out your tongue. Take a deep breath in and breath out through your mouth....AND DROP!

NOW...Let your body become quiet. Rest in the bowl of silent spaghetti. Be so quiet and still. I am going to pour on the rainbow sauce. The sauce is neither too hot nor too cold. I pour the red sauce over your toes, feet, legs, fingers and hands. I pour orange sauce over your lower belly and your lower arms. I pour the color yellow over your upper belly and your upper arms. I pour the color green over your chest and your shoulders. I pour light blue over your neck and chin. I pour Indigo (dark blue) over your face and your forehead. I pour violet over your head and your hair. Now, use your breath to mix the sauce. Make 6-12 breaths as you swirl the rainbow...the rainbow inside of you. After 6-12 breaths, wiggle your spaghetti fingers and spaghetti toes.

Twirl your spaghetti - hug your spaghetti knees into your belly and chest. Roll to the right side. Then sit up in easy chair pose (Sukasana).

SEESAW 16
Upavishtha Konasana

Find a partner for this pose. Sit on your bottom facing your partner. Both partners open their feet out wide, with legs out straight and let your feet touch. Join hands with your partner and gently move back and forth like a seesaw! Try to keep your back long and tall when pulling one another.

Benefits: This is a cooling and calming pose. It deeply releases tension in the inner leg muscles and increases circulation in the hips and lower belly.

Notes: Try to keep your toes pointing towards the sky. Bend your knees a little bit so that when you see-saw back and forth, you bend from your hips rather than your waist.

SNAIL SHELL 36
Ardha Matsyendrasana/ Marichyasana I and III

Sit on your bum with your legs out straight. Bend your left knee and place your foot close to the left hip (you can place the foot further forward if necessary). Be sure you are sitting evenly on your bum. Turn to the left. While keeping your left arm straight,

79

place your left hand on the ground behind your left hip with fingers facing back. Inhale and raise your right arm up. As your breathe out, twist to the left and place your right elbow to the outside of your left knee and look to the left. Or hug your left knee with your right arm. Take 3-6 breaths. Then repeat the pose bending the right leg and twisting to the right.

Benefits: Helps open the shoulders and the upper back. Tones the organs - our body engines - by enhancing blood and fluid circulation in the belly area. Increases flexibility in the back. Increases and balances energy level.

Notes: Keep sitting up tall by moving your hips forward. Avoid holding your breath.

TORTOISE 20
Kurmasana

Sit on your bum with your legs out wide. Bend your knees and place your arms and hands to the inside of your legs. Walk your legs a little closer to your arms. Slide your arms under your legs and bring your hands to the outside of your feet. With your palms down, stretch your arms out to the sides and begin to lengthen your legs. Look forward and give 3-6 snapping breaths - exhaling quickly as you snap your teeth together.

Benefits: Calms and relaxes the mind. Tones the muscles of the back. Massages the belly.

Notes: DO NOT force your legs to go out straight. You can do this pose with your feet together, placing your arms under your legs, wrapping your hands around your feet and putting your head down towards your feet-like a turtle sleeping in the shell (Supta Kurmasana).

TREE 38
Vriksasana

Stand in Mountain pose. Shift your weight into your right foot.

Step 1: Place your left heel on the top of your right foot. Raise your arms up like branches, with your palms facing one another OR palms together over your head OR palms together at your heart.

Step 2: Place your left heel on your right shin. Raise your arms up like branches.

Step 3: Place your left foot on the side of your right lower leg.

Step 4: Place your left foot on your right thigh. AVOID putting your foot against your knee.

Take 3-6 windy breaths and keep your toe roots strong as your balance your tree! Repeat the pose with the right leg down and the left foot up.

Benefits: Strengthens feet and legs. Improves poise, balance and concentration.

Notes: Keep looking out in the same direction at eye level (Dristhi). You can make your branches small (Namaste' at your heart) or make wide branches with your arms out to the sides.

THE RAINBOW INSIDE OF YOU
The Seven Chakras

When we sit in silence and breathe, we find the quiet place inside. It is said in the teachings of yoga that our body is like an instrument. Imagine, that from the bottom of your back to the top of our head, you are like a flute. When you chant the sound OM (AUM), you tune all the notes to one harmony. There are seven notes or wheels (called Chakras in Sanskrit) in our energy body. We do our yoga practice to keep the wheels spinning in balance with one another.

Here is a simple outline of some important aspects of the Seven Chakras:

1. Muladhara Chakra Location: at the base of the back/spine. Element: earth. Color: red. This chakra is connected to the ability we have to take care of ourselves and our need for safety.

2. Svadhisthana Chakra Location: sacrum/lower belly. Element: water. Color: orange. This chakra is connected to our ability to create life and to have a sense of belonging to community, family and friends.

3. Manipura Chakra Location: solar plexis/upper belly. Element: fire. Color: yellow. This chakra is connected to our ability to be creative, self-disciplined, self-confident, and focused on our goals.

4. Anahata Chakra Location: heart/chest. Element: air. Color: green. This chakra is connected to our ability to love, share and care for others.

5. Vishuddha Chakra Location: throat/neck. Element: ether. Color: light blue. This chakra is connected to our ability to communicate our feelings, needs and to speak the truth from the heart.

6. Ajna Chakra Location: third eye/the point between the eyebrows. Element: light. Color: indigo/dark blue. This chakra is connected to our ability to access our imagination and intuition (instinctual inner knowledge).

7. Sahasrara Chakra Location: the top of the head. Element: thought. Color: violet. This chakra is connected to our ability to have faith in ourselves and the mysteries of life and to attain wisdom and understanding.